OUT WEST WITH BARBIE

This is the story of how Barbie and her wonderful horse, Dallas. Came together...

Special Assignment

It was a sad and anxious Barbie who heard the grave words of the vet, when he was called to the stables one evening...

YOUR HORSE IS VERY SICK...FEVER BROUGHT ON BY A CHILL, I'M AFRAID.

OH, MY POOR DALLAS. WILL... WILL HE GET BETTER?

HE MUST BE KEPT WARM, AND IF WE'RE LUCKY, MY DEAR, THE FEVER WILL PASS BY MORNING.

And all through the long night, Barbie sat with her dear four-legged friend...

PLEASE, OH, PLEASE, DON'T LET HIM DIE.

BARBIE, MY DEAR, SHOULDN'T YOU TRY AND GET SOME SLEEP?

NO, I CAN'T LEAVE POOR DALLAS, MRS MATT. HE... HE MEANS SO MUCH TO ME.

BUT WHO'D HAVE THOUGHT WE'D HAVE BEEN SUCH FRIENDS... BACK IN THE BEGINNING...

£3·25

And Barbie's mind flashed back to the time she'd been invited to stay at a Texas ranch by her American friend and fellow model, Judy Forrest...

AFTER THAT HEARTY BREAKFAST OF FLAP-JACKS AND MAPLE SYRUP, WE NEED SOME EXERCISE, BARBIE! CHOOSE A HORSE TO COME RIDING WITH ME!

MMM, I'D LOVE TO.

And her eyes fell on the proud-looking, golden palamino...

OH, ISN'T HE A BEAUTY!

THAT'S DALLAS. BUT I GUESS YOU'D BETTER PICK AGAIN.

HE'S WILD AND UNRIDEABLE, BARBIE!

BUT I'D LIKE TO TRY. MAY I?

OKAY, HONEY. WE CAN SADDLE HIM UP FOR YOU.

...BUT YOU WON'T STAY LONG IN THE SADDLE!

POOR YOU, LAID UP NURSING YOUR BRUISES. BUT I DID WARN YOU ABOUT THAT FOUR-LEGGED FIRECRACKER!

Sure enough...

OOOH!

Which meant Barbie spent the rest of the day...

I KNOW. I'M WHAT KEN CALLS 'A STUBBORN MULESS' AT TIMES.

BUT I ONLY WANTED US TO BE FRIENDS, DALLAS.

AND, BRUISES OR NO BRUISES, TOMORROW I'LL TRY AGAIN.

So. . .

GOOD MORNING, DALLAS! LOOK, I'VE BROUGHT YOU SOME SUGAR.

But. . .

OH, SHAME ON YOU, TURNING YOUR BACK ON ME. DON'T YOU WANT US TO BE FRIENDS?

But that day, **and** the next, it seemed **not** —

OH, YOU MAY LAUGH, BUT YOU'VE GOT TO **STOP** THIS, DO YOU HEAR. I'LL HAVE SO MANY BUMPS AND BRUISES, I WON'T BE ABLE TO MODEL PRETTY CLOTHES FOR A YEAR!

Finally, however. . .

BRAVO, BARBIE! YOU'RE **RIDING** HIM!

YES, I THINK THE DEAR OLD THING GOT TIRED OF SEEING ME BITING THE DUST ALL THE TIME!

And soon the girls were out riding together on the open prairie. . .

GOSH, IT'S SO BIG AND BEAUTIFUL!

THEY USE IT FOR COWBOY MOVIES. GREAT FOR CHASES!

COME ON, RACE YOU TO CACTUS CANYON!

BUT I DON'T KNOW WHERE CACTUS CANYON IS?

I KNOW, THAT'S WHY I'M GOING TO WIN, HA HA!

OH, WE'LL SEE ABOUT THAT, WON'T WE, DALLAS? SHOW HER, BOY!

6

PLEASE, DALLAS. . .OH, PLEASE DON'T DESERT US. H-HELP ME.

Then, just when she thought her tearful cries were in vain. . .Dallas came racing back to their aid. . . .

. . .PROVING THAT HE IS A TRUE FRIEND AFTER ALL!

OH, BARBIE, YOU AND DALLAS SAVED MY LIFE! HOW CAN I EVER REPAY YOU BOTH?

WELL, I DON'T KNOW WHAT HE WANTS, BUT I'D LOVE TO HAVE THE DEAR THING FOR MY VERY OWN. WILL YOU LET ME BUY HIM FROM YOU?

HE'S YOURS — FOR FREE. AND I RECKON HE LIKES THE IDEA TOO!

BUT NOW THERE'S NO-ONE WHO CAN HELP YOU IN RETURN, POOR DALLAS. I. . .I THINK MY HEART IS GOING TO BREAK. . .

But suddenly she felt a familiar nose nuzzling her cheek. . .

DALLAS! YOU'RE WELL AGAIN. . .THE FEVER HAS GONE!

OH, I'M SO HAPPY. I THOUGHT I'D LOST YOU. . .BUT YOU CAME BACK TO ME JUST LIKE YOU DID BEFORE, DEAR OLD FRIEND!

THE END

SKIPPER'S PUZZLE

CLUES ACROSS

1. Time-saving device for making clothes
7. Animal who gives us wool
10. Barbie's photographer boyfriend
11. Huge, enormous — the opposite of a dwarf
14. If three is a trio, two is a __?
16. Fruit of a tree — e.g. brazils, cashews
19. To colour material
22. Book showing maps of the world
25. You need this to dry you after a bath
27. Sea that laps France, Italy, Greece, etc

CLUES DOWN

2. Saturday and Sunday together are called __?
3. Cold place where you go to skate
4. Piece of furniture — Barbie sits at it to do her make-up
5. Fairground entertainment — you ride down and round and round
8. Thin garment worn underneath a dress or skirt
21. Building where plays are performed

THE FAIRY'S PROMISE

11

12

SUPERSTAR KEN!

Ken had been asked to take photographs of the pop star, Tiger Taylor, and Barbie was along for the fashion shots...

MORE! MORE!

THAT WAS HIS FINAL NUMBER. WASN'T HE GREAT, KEN?

YEAH, NOT BAD! LET'S GO AND SEE HIM.

And later...

THAT'S FINE...GREAT! I THINK WE'VE GOT THROUGH ALL THE OUTFITS NOW.

YOU MUST BE EXHAUSTED, TIGER.

SORRY I CAN'T STOP, FOLKS! I'LL GET GRABBED IF I HANG ABOUT HERE.

SEE YOU IN YOUR DRESSING ROOM, TIGER!

I MEAN, YOU GET THE RED CARPET TREATMENT WHEREVER YOU GO! YOU STAY IN THE BEST HOTELS, EAT OUT IN FANTASTIC RESTAURANTS, GET ALL THE GIRLS AFTER YOU — JUST GIVE ME HALF A CHANCE!

HEY, D'YOU MEAN THAT?

SURE I DO, WHY?

I MUST ADMIT I COULD REALLY GO FOR A SPOT OF REST AND RELAXATION — THOUGH THERE'S NOT MUCH CHANCE OF THAT, WITH THE LIFE I LEAD.

GO ON, IT'S NOT THAT BAD, SURELY?!

BECAUSE THIS PLACE JUST HAPPENS TO BE MY HOME TOWN — AND I'D ALMOST GIVEN UP HOPE OF SLIPPING AWAY FROM THE FANS TO SEE MY FAMILY...

SO IF KEN...

TIGER TYLOR

TIGER TYLOR

RIGHT! IF KEN STOOD IN FOR ME. . .KEPT THE FANS OFF MY TRAIL FOR THE EVENING. . .

WELL, HERE'S YOUR CHANCE TO BE A POP STAR, KEN. WHAT D'YOU THINK?

LEAD ME TO IT!

So with some of Tiger's clothes — and a wig kept for when Tiger's hair was out of sorts. . .

TIGER — MEET TIGER!

HEY, YOU REALLY LOOK LIKE ME!

SO WHERE DO I GO FIRST?

YOU'VE GOT A ROOM BOOKED AT THE AMBASSADOR HOTEL. I'LL GIVE YOU SOME MONEY TO PAY FOR IT — AND THEN A TABLE FOR DINNER AT PEPPERMINT PALACE.

AND WHAT WILL YOU DO, TIGER?

I'LL BE HAVING SAUSAGES AND MASH AT MY MUM'S — AND THEN PUTTING MY FEET UP IN FRONT OF THE TELLY!

WHILE I'M AT THE AMBASSADOR HOTEL AND PEPPERMINT PALACE! YOU MUST BE MAD!

TIGER TYLOR

MY CHAUFFEUR–DRIVEN ROLLS IS OUT THE FRONT. I'LL GIVE YOU TEN MINUTES AND THEN SLIP OUT THE BACK WAY.

A ROLLS! YIPPEE!

EXIT

And so. . .

COME ON, BARBIE!

TIGER! TIGER! OVER HERE! WE LOVE YOU, TIGER!

JUMP IN QUICKLY, SIR!

JUST MADE IT THERE, SIR!

DID YOU HEAR THAT, BARBIE? THEY ALL LOVE ME!

ACTUALLY, I HATE TO SAY THIS, BUT I THINK IT'S TIGER THEY LOVE, KEN!

15

SHAKIN'
STEVENS

Barbie

TEST YOURSELF

ARE YOU A STAR?

1. You're dancing and singing along to a favourite record, thinking you're alone. Suddenly you realise you have an audience, the window cleaner! Do you:
a. Hide your embarrassment by pretending it's your daily exercise routine?
b. Go hot and cold and rush out of the room?
c. Carry on with your act, and expect applause?

Twinkle, twinkle, shy or star — how we wonder which you are!

b. Ask him for a trim?
c. Ask him to copy an outrageous hairstyle you've seen in a magazine?

2. Your best friend's invited you to her party. Do you:
a. Turn up early to help make sure that things get going smoothly?
b. Go with a friend so you've got some moral support?
c. Arrive late so that everyone notices your grand entrance?

3. Mum's made an appointment for you to have your hair trimmed. When you get to the hairdressers, do you:
a. Insist on the latest style?

4. On holiday you notice a poster advertising a talent contest. Do you:
a. Go along and watch? It might be a giggle.
b. Keep well away? You hate to see people making fools of themselves.
c. Enter your name and start rehearsing right away?

5. They're taking a photo of your class at school. Do you:
a. Brush your hair and try to look human!?
b. Hide behind your tallest classmate?
c. Push your way to the front, smiling from ear to ear?

6. If your sister or a friend won a small part in a tv play, would you:
a. Be really pleased for her?
b. Be amazed? You wonder how she's got the nerve.
c. Be madly jealous? Why can't it be you?

7. Your school is having a charity fair and you're asked to help in any way you can. Do you:
a. Set up an Aunt Sally stall with your friends?
b. Bake some cakes for sale?
c. Get loads of people to sponsor you for a dance marathon to take place at the fair?

8. It's a family party and Dad says everybody has to take turns at being an entertainer. Do you:

a. Mumble an old joke, blushing a bit?
b. Offer to do the washing up so you can get out of it?
c. Steal the show with songs, impersonations and funny stories?

SCORE

Mostly a's: You're not one to be overlooked, though you hate to appear a fool. You leave the starring rôles to your friends.

Mostly b's: Seems as if you've lost your twinkle — if you ever had it in the first place, that is. You prefer to hide shyly in the shadows.

Mostly c's: You stand out in a crowd, and that's fine by you. What people think of you isn't important as long as you have their attention. And you usually succeed!

U2 A few words from Bono...

I was christened Paul Hewson and was born in Dublin, Ireland. I first met the rest of the band at Mount Pleasant Comprehensive School in Dublin. We really had nothing in common to begin with except for the fact that we all sang in the choir!

We formed U2 the same year as Bob Geldof was forming the Boomtown Rats. It was 1978 and that was the year we entered the Guinness and Harp Talent Contest.

At the time I lost my voice and we sounded awful — but we were still offered a contract.

So when U2 appeared on 'Top of the Pops', did it make them millionaires overnight?

I remember when we were on 'Top of the Pops' — we had to get the bus home! But we're now considered the best rock band in the world — and we're not going to disagree with that!

ROOM TO MOVE

Barbie's just bought a new flat — and she needs your help to furnish it! Hidden in the box of letters below are twenty one items of furniture and fittings that Barbie will need. Some are spelt out across, some down and some diagonally. And to give you a start the word CHAIR is already shown.

```
P  E  L  W  U  N  S  W  Y  A  D  L  Q  U  I
H  M  I  R  R  O  R  A  S  B  E  X  A  R  R
C  I  B  L  O  V  T  S  C  I  W  S  C  M  I
U  E  E  A  L  L  Y  H  H  E  O  F  U  M  P
R  B  D  U  T  Z  P  I  A  N  O  P  P  T  W
T  C  A  Y  M  H  E  N  I  A  F  G  B  E  A
A  A  P  A  W  H  S  G  R  R  V  O  O  L  R
I  R  I  Q  U  I  I  M  H  U  R  M  A  E  D
N  P  C  A  E  D  L  A  N  I  G  J  R  V  R
S  E  T  T  E  E  K  C  S  W  R  A  D  I  O
J  T  U  O  A  Z  S  H  P  T  I  V  U  S  B
B  C  R  I  K  B  L  I  T  H  O  V  W  I  E
E  P  E  M  G  X  L  N  N  O  E  O  T  O  J
B  O  O  K  C  A  S  E  H  K  E  A  L  N  Y
A  D  R  E  F  R  I  D  G  E  R  A  T  O  R
```

SOLUTION ON PAGE 79

Skipper

Skipper looked across the practice room and frowned at her friend. ''I wish I could dance like you, Bryony,'' she said. ''I've never seen anyone so light. When you jump in the air it looks as though someone's pulling you up on a string.''

''It's only practice,'' Bryony said, doing another of her leaps across to the barre. ''You could dance like me if you tried.''

Skipper shook her head. ''I never could! Anyway, you're so dedicated. You live for ballet, don't you?''

Bryony smiled. ''I suppose I do — and anyway, coming here so often gets me out of the house.''

''Why should you want to get out of your house?'' Skipper asked curiously.

''It's too crowded!'' Bryony held onto the barre and did a perfect demi-plié, then bent over so that her hair brushed on the floor. ''I've got four brothers and sisters — all younger than me. When I'm at home there's no room to do anything. No peace to even *think*.''

''So Madame lets you come here whenever you like?''

Bryony nodded. ''I think she's only too pleased that the practice room gets used. She said she's got everything here, so it's silly for the room to be standing empty half the week.''

''Mmm, I see,'' Skipper said. She watched in admiration as Bryony stood in arabesque position, then went along to the changing room for a shower. She knew that Bryony would be there until Madame locked up at six o'clock that evening.

Isabelle, one of the other girls in the class, was just coming out of the shower when Skipper went in.

''I suppose Bryony's still practising,'' she said nastily.

and the surprise

"What a crawler! Always trying to get in with Madame, she is."

"She's not!" Skipper said. "She just really enjoys ballet. It's not just a class to her, it's a way of life."

"Madame's little pet!" Isabelle said. "She always gets the lead in the end-of-term productions, too!"

"Well, she's our best dancer," Skipper said loyally, hanging up her leotard. "Who else is there?"

"Me, of course," Isabelle said.

Skipper looked at Isabelle. She was a strong dancer all right — but she was too big, too aggressive for the sort of ballet that Madame always favoured. "I can't see you as Giselle," Skipper said.

"I'm a terrific dancer," Isabelle boasted. "Everyone says so. In my last class they recommended that I should try and get in a ballet school."

Skipper raised her eyebrows. "Madame never gives me a chance! She doesn't let me dance the fiery sort of roles I want to."

"Perhaps next term," Skipper murmured, going into the shower. As far as she was concerned, no-one danced anywhere near as well as Bryony.

After class the following week Madame stood at the front and held up her hand for everyone to be quiet.

"I've got some exciting news, girls!" she said. "I didn't tell you before class because I didn't want everyone to get excited so that their dancing would suffer." She motioned them all to sit on the floor.

"You remember two weeks ago we had a lady observer in the audience," she said, and the girls nodded. "Well, I let you all think she was a parent wanting to send her daughter here, but she wasn't." She hesitated and took a deep breath. "It was someone from the National Ballet School and she wants to offer one of you a scholarship!"

There were excited gasps from the girls. Skipper looked sideways at Bryony, feeling she knew already who it must be.

"Bryony Williams, stand up, please!" Madame said dramatically. "You are the pupil she has chosen!"

As the girls broke into excited chatter and started clapping, Bryony reluctantly got to her feet.

"But Madame . . ." she began.

"They are willing to pay half her fees for five years," Madame went on, beaming. "It's a marvellous offer and one that will ensure a great future for Bryony. She's been working really well lately and I'm sure we all realise how much she deserves this scholarship."

The girls all gathered round Bryony excitedly, slapping her on the back and saying well done — all except Isabelle, Skipper noticed. She also noticed that Bryony didn't look too happy, for some reason. Maybe the good news hadn't sunk in yet, though.

The following Friday, Skipper met Bryony before class.

"What did your mum and dad say about the scholarship?" Skipper asked. "Bet they were thrilled!"

Bryony shook her head sadly. "They *were* pleased," she said. "But there's no way I can go."

Skipper looked at her in astonishment. "But why not?"

"Because of the cost," Bryony said. "Even though I'm getting half the fees paid, it's still an incredible amount of money. And then there are extra lessons to pay for and the uniform and all the ballet clothes I'd need." She shook her head sadly, "It's out of the question. You see, it's all my Mum and Dad can do to send me here each week."

Skipper put her arm round her friend. "But that's *awful*. Isn't there a way to get more of the fees paid?"

Bryony shrugged. "Even if there was I couldn't go. Mum and Dad couldn't afford the fares for me to get there every day."

"Oh dear," Skipper said. "Have you told Madame?"

Bryony nodded. "She wasn't very happy about it. It would have been such an achievement for her to have got one of her pupils a place at the National."

The two girls went in and got changed, and after an hour's hard work on the barre Madame called them together to talk about the end-of-term production. "Everyone's shaping up well," she said, "but I want you to be prepared to come in and do extra practice whenever you can."

Everyone said they would

and then Madame announced that Bryony would not be taking up her place at the National. "It's very sad," she said, "but I want you to know that I have written to the National and asked if they'd be prepared to take Isabelle, instead."

Isabelle looked round at everyone, a smug smile on her face.

"If she works hard maybe she can do as well as Bryony would have done," Madame said, and then looked at Bryony and sighed. "Such a pity . . . such a pity."

Bryony jumped up and ran out saying she had to be home early — but Skipper couldn't have been the only one to notice that she had her hanky up to her eyes as she ran.

Skipper made up her mind there and then that she had to do something, if only to stop the awful Isabelle taking that ballet school place!

When she went home she spent a long time thinking, and then she asked Barbie for some of her best notepaper and locked herself in her bedroom to write what she would only tell everyone was a 'very important letter.'

Meanwhile the rehearsals for Giselle were stepped up to two a week. Skipper was only playing one of the wood spirits so she wasn't always needed, but Bryony went in twice a week and also put in a lot of extra time in the practice room on her own.

Isabelle got unbearable.

"Madame hasn't heard from the National yet but she's expecting to any day," she said one afternoon. "Once they see me in action I'm sure they'll

realise that they should have offered me the scholarship in the first place."

"Fancy yourself, don't you?" one of the other girls said.

"I'm just being honest," Isabelle replied. "Bryony might be good at those flimsy romantic roles but it takes someone like me with a bit of stamina to really put some oomph into a ballet."

Skipper looked across at Bryony in concern. Her friend was looking pale — as if the events of the past weeks had been a worry to her.

"It'll be all right," she said in her ear on their way out. "Isabelle won't get that place!"

"How d'you know that?" Bryony said. "I bet she will! Madame will put in a good word for her — she's determined that *someone* from here will go to the National."

"Just you wait and see," Skipper said. She would have liked to have said more, but she wasn't at all sure of what was going to happen — she still hadn't had a reply to her letter.

At the end-of-term performance of Giselle the curtain opened and Skipper, from her position in the back row of dancers, strained her eyes to see who was in the audience. She recognised some of the parents, local shopkeepers, even the Mayor, but she couldn't see the very important person she was looking for. Maybe she hadn't received the letter . . . maybe she had but was much too busy and important to bother about little girls like Bryony.

The music began and Skipper saw Madame's anxious face watching them from the wings.

"It's all right, Madame," Skipper wanted to tell her. "Bryony won't let you down!"

She didn't either, she danced a beautiful Giselle, frail, delicate and haunting. Skipper was sure there wasn't a dry eye in the audience when she finally sank to the ground and died.

As the music faded away the audience burst into loud applause and the girls each walked off the stage in turn.

"Magnificent!" Madame hugged each of them as they came off. "You were all marvellous!" She frowned slightly at Isabelle. "Although *you* tried to upstage Bryony a little. I saw you kept dancing in front of her!"

"Did I, Madame?" Isabelle said carelessly. "Still, I expect the audience enjoyed it."

Madame didn't hear her, she was kissing Bryony on both cheeks and saying she'd never danced as beautifully or as well. "Ah, if only you could have gone to the National," she said, wiping away an emotional tear. "Who knows what sort of future you'd have had?"

Everyone went on stage for a curtain call and Madame went out, too, and curtseyed to everyone. It was while the audience were still on their feet applauding that someone left their seat at the back and began to make their way to the stage.

The woman was tall and dark and magnificently dressed in a full-length fur coat and hat. Even those in the audience who didn't recognise her knew that she must be *someone*.

Skipper's heart missed a beat. She'd come! She'd really come!

Madame, in the middle of another curtsey, stopped, still with bent knees, and seemed to freeze in that position. Her jaw dropped open.

The figure climbed up the steps leading to the stage and took Madame's hand. Madame straightened up, still looking stunned.

"May I congratulate you on a marvellous performance," the visitor said. Madame hesitated and then rose magnificently to the occasion. She looked at the hushed, expectant audience.

"We are indeed honoured . . ." she began, and then she looked once more at her distinguished guest and shook her head as if she couldn't quite believe it, ". . . to have with us this evening, the prima ballerina of the Royal Company, Dame Margareta Fontana!"

There was a wild cheer from the audience. Even those who weren't real ballet fans had seen Margareta Fontana that week in a Royal Variety Performance. Dame Fontana bowed deeply, blew a kiss to the audience.

"I have come in response to a letter from a young fan," she said. "I was told an unfortunate tale about a scholarship offered which could not be taken up and I decided to come and see for myself just what the child had to offer."

She paused for effect, then held up her hand. "Bryony Williams, will you please come forward!" she cried. "Never have I seen Giselle danced with such grace by one so young. You shall take up the scholarship!"

Bryony seemed to be rooted to the spot. Skipper pushed her forward. "Go on!" she urged. "It's you she's talking about!"

"I have decided to give a gala performance," Dame Fontana went on. "And all the proceeds shall go to furthering this young girl's career. I will see to it that she reaches the very height of the profession!"

A stumbling, shy Bryony went forward and, grasping Dame Fontana's hand, gave a low curtsey. Someone in the front row was moved enough to throw a bunch of daffodils onto the stage and then the whole audience erupted. It was like the first night at Covent Garden Opera House.

"It was just *magic*!" a starry-eyed Bryony said to Skipper afterwards. "Me up there on stage with Dame Margareta Fontana, *me* taking a curtain call with her!"

"Some people have all the luck," a grumpy voice said from behind them, and they looked round to see Isabelle pulling on her track suit. "If Madame hadn't been so stuck on silly, flowery roles I'd have been the one chosen!"

Skipper and Bryony both ignored her.

"However did she find out about the scholarship, though?" Bryony wanted to know. "However did she find me here?"

Skipper looked at her and giggled. "As you said — it must have been magic!" she said, and she did a quick, happy leap in the air where no-one could see her.

GEORGE

Believe it or not, George Michael never imagined that one day he'd become a heart-throb. "I was very shy as a teenager," he remembers. "I had no confidence, you see. I didn't think that I was particularly good looking and anyway, all the girls were after Andrew!"

George was talking about when the boys were at secondary school in North London where the two of them first met each other.

VERY CLOSE

George was born on 25th June, 1963 in Bushey, Herts. His family still live there, but he now lives in London. He is still very close to his family, especially sister Melanie — well he must be because he lets her cut his hair!

George likes going on holiday with Andrew and going out to eat. He says, "I used to enjoy going to nightclubs but I must admit that I prefer somewhere quieter these days."

George has only one ambition and that's to carry on being successful.

ALL ABOUT WHAM!

ANDREW

Like George, Andrew Ridgeley was born in Bushey, Herts, but on 26th January 1963. Andrew says, "The most important thing about Wham! is the fact that George and I are such good friends." You would think after all these years of knowing each other, Andrew and George would be sick of the sight of each other, but they're not — far from it in fact.

GOOD FRIENDS

"Oh, we have arguments all right," Andrew admits. "But then again most lifelong friends do. The good thing is we always make up very quickly. We still go out together when we're not working. Our manager calls us Butch Cassidy and the Sundance Kid!"

Andrew's ambition is to try and do a spot of acting, but he says, "For the moment I'm quite happy with life."

Fan Club

Stop Press

Wham have of course split up since this feature went to press, but we thought you'd like to keep this picture of the boys!

DAYS WITH

The Story of a girl and a kitten

Sunday

I've started on a campaign to persuade Mum to let me have one of Mrs Duncan-down-the-road's kittens. I went down to see them today and they're just gorgeous. Mitzi, the mother cat, is tortoiseshell, so one of the kittens is a reddish brown colour, one is nearly all white and the best one is a lovely pale grey colour and very fluffy. Mrs Duncan said I could name them for her so I've called them Rusty (the red one), Musty (the white one) and Dusty. Dusty's the one I want!

Monday

Put my first plan into action at breakfast this morning. Did this by talking about my friends at school and telling Mum what pets they had.

"If only *I* had a pet," I finished wistfully. "It would make up for not having a brother or sister."

She laughed. "I know you," she said. "It would be fine for a week or so and then I'd be the one going out in all weathers taking it for walks."

"I wouldn't want a dog," I said. "I'd rather have something small."

"Something in a cage would be worse! I know *exactly* who'd end up cleaning it out!"

"I don't want anything in a cage," I said. "Just a nice quiet little . . ."

"Goldfish!" she said. "You can have a goldfish."

"You can't cuddle a goldfish! I don't want one of those. I was thinking more of something fluffy, like a kitten . . ."

Mum gave a shriek. "You know I hate cats!" she said. "I can't stand the things!"

"But, Mum . . ."

"Enough!" she said, holding up her hand. "Time to get ready for school — and I don't want to hear any more about cats."

Tuesday

Went to see the kittens again. They've started getting out of their cardboard box now and they're crawling everywhere. Mitzi spends all her time going off to rescue them and hauling them back by the scruffs of their necks.

"Will you be wanting one of them?" Mrs Duncan asked. "They're nearly old enough to leave their mother and I'm getting lots of enquiries, especially about Dusty."

"Oh, I do want one," I said. "It's just persuading Mum that *she* wants one."

"You'll have to let me know by the end of the week," Mrs Duncan said.

Wednesday

Stepped up my campaign over breakfast. Told Mum that I'd been feeling really lonely since I'd started at my new school.

"Everyone lives so far away," I sighed pathetically. "I can never have friends home for tea now."

"What's that, love?" Dad asked.

"I'm just a bit lonely," I said in a sad little voice. "If only I could have a pet."

"Good idea," Dad said, much to my surprise. "It would give you something to be responsible for looking after."

"Len!" Mum said at once. "That's all I want — you siding with Melanie. I've told her I don't like cats." She shuddered. "I can't bear them near me."

I looked at Dad pleadingly, a sort of 'Help me!' look, and he gave me a 'Well, what can I do?' look back.

Thursday

Two of the kittens have gone! Went in to Mrs Duncan's on my way home from school today and there was just Mitzi and Dusty there in the box.

"Rusty and Musty have gone to new homes," Mrs Duncan said, "and I'm going away on Saturday so if you can't have Dusty I'll have to let her go to the next person who asks for her."

"I'll talk to Mum tonight!" I said, all in a panic. "Don't let anyone take Dusty away!"

Went home and wrote a long list for Mum of all the things I'd do if she would only let me have a kitten. It included cleaning the cupboards in the sitting room, washing the kitchen floor, cleaning the cooker, dusting and doing the shopping for a month. It also said that I'd go without Christmas and birthday presents this year if only I could have Dusty.

Left it by Mum's breakfast plate and went to bed early.

Friday

The list wasn't on the table and Mum didn't say a thing about it this morning. She *must* have found it.

There was a lovely picture of some kittens in a basket in my comic and I pointed it out to her.

"Aren't they *sweet?*" I said. "You couldn't not love those dear little fluffy things, could you?"

"Certainly I could," she said. "Because they're not going to stay little and fluffy for

DUSTY

ever. They're going to get big and grow nasty sharp claws and strong teeth.'' She shivered. ''All the better to bite me with.''

I sighed. This campaign isn't going too well.

Saturday

Decision day. Really didn't know *what* to do when I got up. Mum was in a bad mood so I didn't dare say anything else to her. Went along to Mrs Duncan's straight after breakfast.

''Sorry, dear,'' she said, ''but I've got someone coming at lunchtime for Dusty.''

''But . . . but . . . '' I stammered.

''It's a shame, I know you wanted her, but I'm going away this evening and Mitzi's going into kennels for a week,'' she said. ''I had to find someone to take care of Dusty.''

I crossed my fingers behind my back. ''But . . . but I was coming to tell you I *can* have her!'' I said desperately. ''I spoke to Mum last night and persuaded her.''

A smile spread across Mrs Duncan's face. ''Well, that's good news, dear,'' she said, ''I'm so pleased for you I'll ring up the person who enquired and tell them Dusty's already gone.''

''Oh, please!'' I said in relief, and I picked up Dusty and hugged her until she gave a little squeaky miaow.

''Will you take her with you now, then?'' Mrs Duncan asked.

I looked at her in alarm. What on earth was I going to do with Dusty?

''That would be easier, wouldn't it? Save you coming back.'' She gave me a list of the things Dusty ate and how to look after her for the first couple of days, then before I knew it I was walking up the path with a kitten hidden under my coat.

Mum wasn't in, luckily, so I took Dusty straight upstairs, found a box for a litter tray and another larger one for her bed, and put her in it. She fell asleep straight away so I pushed the box under the bed and sat down on the floor to have a quiet panic. What was I going to do? Mum would go mad!

Raided my piggy bank and slipped out to the corner shop to get some tins of kitten food and also a spare pint of milk.

"There! I didn't know you had a cat!" Mrs Jenkins said when I went to pay for them. "Your mother never mentioned it."

"It's a surprise for her," I said weakly.

"Well I never — and I didn't think she liked cats!" Mrs Jenkins exclaimed.

I spent nearly all day in my room. I told Mum I was working on a project (well, it was almost true). I tried to get Dad on his own to tell him, but I could never seem to time it properly, so I just stayed out of the way and played with Dusty. She's so lovely!

Sunday

This morning I showed Dusty again how to use her litter box and she performed beautifully. She sleeps a lot — like a newborn baby does, I suppose — and I never get tired of watching her. When she's had something to eat, she sits and washes her face, daintily going behind each ear in turn. Sometimes when she bends over to wash her back legs she overbalances, rolls over and can't seem to get straight again.

Went downstairs for lunch and Mum asked me what the attraction was in my room.

"You haven't been out of it

for two days," she said. "Don't tell me you've been cleaning it!"

"Just a bit," I said cautiously.

"Really? This I've got to see," Mum said sarcastically, but I quickly changed the subject.

Spent a lot of the afternoon worrying about tomorrow. I can't expect to keep Dusty hidden away while I'm at school. After tea Dad and I were washing up and I was just about to whisper to him that I had something important to tell him when there was a big scream from upstairs. Dad and I both rushed out, but I *knew* what it was.

Mum stood at the top of the stairs flapping her apron. "There's something in your room, Melanie!" she shouted. "It jumped on my foot when I opened the door!"

I ran upstairs two at a time and burst into tears at the top.

"I'm sorry!" I wailed. "I wanted to tell you but I didn't know how to. I had to take her or Mrs Duncan would have given her to someone else. Oh, Mum, *please* let me keep her!"

Dad came up then and we all started talking at once and they were both really cross with me. Mum wanted me to take Dusty straight back but Mrs Duncan's away now, thank goodness, so we've got to wait until she comes back.

I know I've only had Dusty for two days but I can't bear the thought of being without her.

Monday

Fed Dusty first thing, cleaned out her litter tray and left her with lots of toys to play with.

"I don't want to see that animal down here!" Mum said at breakfast, and I promised that she'd stay in my room.

"She sleeps a lot," I said. "And then she'll just play with her things."

"I don't want any mess up there!" Mum grumbled next. "Cats are destructive. They spring on things and claw at them."

"Her claws aren't strong enough to cause any damage," I said. "And when she springs on things she's only playing. She jumped on your slippers because they're furry — she thought they were something to play with."

"Humph!" Mum said.

When I came home Dusty was asleep, but when she woke up she was really pleased to see me — she licked my hand with her little rough tongue!

Tuesday

"I heard that cat running about in your room today," Mum said. "It sounded as if it was running up and down the curtains."

"She's called Dusty," I said. "And if she was running about I expect it's because she's bored."

"I suppose she couldn't come . . ." Dad began, but Mum gave him one of her looks.

"All I hope is that Mrs Duncan comes home early," she said.

Wednesday

I read in one of my books that kittens need lots of fresh air and exercise so I'm worried about Dusty being shut up in my room all the time. I've made a race-course for her. It's a circuit going through a plastic tube, under the bed, over a shoe-box, under a tunnel made from my bedside rug and over a pile of books. I opened the window wide for the fresh air part of it and started her off, then collapsed in a fit of giggles while I was trying to show her how to go round the course.

I suddenly realised that Mum had opened my door and was

standing there watching us. Dusty was lying on her back kicking away at a cotton wool ball she'd found on her way round.

"What a funny, *tiny* little thing," Mum said. "It looks more like a hamster than a cat."

I looked at her. "Would you let me have a hamster for a pet?"

"I don't know about that," Mum said.

When she'd gone I found a photograph of a hamster in my pet book. Maybe if I could somehow flatten Dusty's ears, tie her tail up a bit . . . no, Mum would never believe me!

Thursday

"I bought a ball for that thing in your room," Mum said today. "The woman in the pet shop said it's got cat mint in it — they like cat mint."

"Oh, Mum!" I said, amazed. "Does this mean . . . "

"Yes, she'll be able to take it with her when she goes back to Mrs Duncan's," Mum said.

I went upstairs and gave it to Dusty. She loved it. First she chased it round the room for a half-hour and tired herself out so much that she just rolled over and fell asleep on the spot. Went down to tell Mum how much she'd enjoyed it.

"I know," Mum said. "I let her have it to play with while you were at school."

I can't make Mum out sometimes.

Friday

Woken up by Dusty licking my face. Felt like crying when I thought of it being her last day with me. My only hope is that Mrs Duncan won't come back — maybe she'll enjoy her holiday so much that she'll stay away for good.

Moped about at school today and could hardly bring myself to speak to anyone. I've got used to having Dusty now. I really love her. If she has to go back I don't know what I'll do!

Stayed in my room all evening so I'd be with her every moment that I could. Went to sleep with her sitting on my head.

Saturday

Crept downstairs but couldn't eat any breakfast.

"Mrs Duncan's home!" Mum said. "I've just seen her going by in her son's car."

Didn't say anything, *couldn't*, or I would have burst out crying.

"If you've got that cat's cases packed, it can go back straight away," Mum went on.

Went back upstairs and sat and stared at Dusty asleep on my worktop, curled into a tight little ball and looking like a grey fluffy powder puff.

"Ready?" Mum called up, but I just sat there and couldn't move.

"I said are you ready, Melanie?" Mum called again.

I took a deep breath, picked up Dusty and went downstairs more miserable than I've ever been in my life.

"Well, what are you waiting for?" Mum said. "Put that thing down in its bed and start turning out my cupboards. After that you've got the kitchen floor to wash and the shopping to do and — what else was it?"

"Oh, Mum!" I cried.

"Into its bed!" she commanded, and I looked round and on the floor was a small basket with a pink cushion in it. "If it's got to live here I don't want a tatty old cardboard box around the place."

"But I didn't think you . . ."

"I wanted to teach you a lesson," she said. "It was very naughty of you to bring it home without asking, *very* naughty — but, well," her voice softened, "it's not a bad little thing and I'll probably get used to it."

"Do you want to hold her?" I asked eagerly, hardly believing my luck.

"Certainly not!" Mum shuddered. "Not yet anyway!"

LLOYD COLE & THE COMMOTIONS

Barbie

A VILLAGE STORE IS USUALLY THE HEART OF THE PLACE. I'LL INTRODUCE MYSELF TO THE SHOP-KEEPER, AND MAYBE HE'LL TELL THE OTHER VILLAGERS THAT WE'VE JUST MOVED IN.

GOOD — GOOD AFTERNOON. I'M KERRY SIMPSON. I'VE JUST MOVED INTO POACHER'S COTTAGE WITH MY FATHER.

But the old man completely ignored her. . .

WHAT A RUDE MAN! HE'S IGNORING ME. I'LL TAKE THIS CAULIFLOWER AND LEAVE THE MONEY BY THE TILL.

HERE'S SOMEONE WHO'LL TALK TO ME! A VICAR ALWAYS LIKES TO WELCOME NEW PARISHIONERS.

HELLO — OH!

DAD WAS RIGHT TO WARN ME. IT'S REALLY HURTFUL TO BE SNUBBED WHEN YOU OFFER THE HAND OF FRIENDSHIP. WELL, I WON'T GIVE ANYONE ELSE THE CHANCE.

JUST LOOK AT HER WITH HER NOSE IN THE AIR! STUCK UP THING!

ISN'T THAT ONE OF THE NEW PEOPLE FROM POACHER'S COTTAGE?

DEAR ME, I NEVER NOTICED, MISS BELLCHAMBER. I WAS BUSY WORKING OUT MY SERMON.

And this is where Sidney comes into the story, for he belonged to Miss Bellchamber. . .

POACHER'S COTTAGE IS RATHER REMOTE, SIDNEY. THAT GIRL COULD FIND IT DIFFICULT TO BECOME PART OF VILLAGE LIFE UNLESS SOMEONE HELPS THINGS ALONG.

34

35

36

WHAT ARE YOU DOING OUT ON YOUR OWN, SIDNEY? YOU'RE RUINING MY SHOP.

I'M SORRY. I'M SUPPOSED TO BE TAKING HIM BACK TO MISS BELLCHAMBER, BUT HE GOT AWAY.

YOU'LL HAVE TO SPEAK UP, DEAR. MISTER FROGGIT'S AS DEAF AS A POST. HE REFUSES TO WEAR HIS DEAF-AID.

SO HE WASN'T ACTUALLY IGNORING ME, THE FIRST TIME I CAME IN HERE. HE JUST DIDN'T HEAR ME!

COME ON, YOU BAD LAD! SEE WHAT I'VE GOT FOR YOU.

WHAT ON EARTH IS HE OFFERING SIDNEY? WHATEVER IT IS, SIDNEY LIKES IT!

YOU'LL DO ANYTHING FOR SOME BARLEY SUGAR, WON'T YOU SIDNEY!

IN THAT CASE, YOU'D BETTER GIVE THIS YOUNG GIRL A POCKET FULL! MISS BELLCHAMBER WENT OFF ON THE DINSHAM BUS, AN HOUR AGO, SO IT LOOKS LIKE SHE'S STUCK WITH SIDNEY!

So later, at Poacher's Cottage. . .

I COULDN'T JUST ABANDON SIDNEY IN THE MIDDLE OF THE VILLAGE, DAD. I EXPECT MISS BELLCHAMBER WILL BE BACK IN A DAY OR TWO.

JUST KEEP THAT ANIMAL OUT OF MY WAY, THEN!

But next morning. . .

OH NO! THAT OLD SHED MUST HAVE BEEN ROTTEN. SIDNEY'S JUST KICKED HIS WAY OUT AND ESCAPED.

THANK GOODNESS HE HASN'T GOT FAR — BUT WHAT ON EARTH IS THAT DRAPED ALL AROUND HIM?

37

THE END

40

THE RUINED CHRISTMAS

It was the day before Christmas Eve. Susan Kemp's father had been working abroad, but he planned to be home for the holiday...

I'VE NEARLY FINISHED DAD'S SCARF. I HOPE HE'LL LIKE IT.

AFTER SIX MONTHS IN THE FAR EAST, HE'LL BE FEELING THE COLD. I SHOULD THINK IT'LL BE THE PERFECT PRESENT.

IT'S GOING TO BE A PERFECT CHRISTMAS ALTOGETHER, MUM! EVEN DOWN TO THE SNOW. IT'S GETTING QUITE THICK NOW.

That night, as she packed Dad's present...

TOMORROW MORNING YOU'LL BE HOME, DAD! I JUST CAN'T WAIT.

MAYBE WE SHOULD GO AND DIG UP OUR SPECIAL FIR TREE BEFORE THE SNOW GETS TOO DEEP.

OH NO MUM, THAT'S DAD'S JOB! IT'S TRADITIONAL THAT HE DOES THAT ON CHRISTMAS EVE, AND THEN WE DECORATE IT.

But next day...

THAT WAS DAD ON THE PHONE, DEAR.

WHERE IS HE? WHY ISN'T HE HERE? IT'S ALMOST LUNCH TIME AND WE STILL HAVE TO FIX THE TREE...

THE SNOW'S GOT SO DEEP, HIS PLANE COULDN'T LAND. IT WAS DIVERTED TO ANOTHER AIRPORT, MILES AWAY, AND NOW THE ROADS ARE BLOCKED.

43

45

SHEENA AND THE DREAMING CHAIR

Sheena was quite upset when her mum told her that Uncle Charlie was dead. She hadn't known him all that well — he was a bit of a quiet man and kept himself to himself — but what she had known about him, she'd liked.

The last time Sheena had seen him was in the summer when she had been invited to his house for tea with some of her cousins. Sheena didn't meet her cousins very often, because for various reasons her mum didn't get on well with the rest of the family, and when she saw them that summer Sheena was quite relieved that she didn't!

●

There were five of them, the three Maxwell children, loud, bad-mannered and bossy, and two Chartwell-Smyths, very well-to-do and looking as if they had a permanent nasty smell under their noses. Sheena had felt like a mouse amongst them — a pale grey, timid mouse with nothing much to say for herself. The five of them tried to outdo each other talking about holidays they'd been on, things they had and places they'd visited and Sheena honestly didn't think she could say much to compete with them. Since her dad had died four years previously, money had been tight and holidays non-existent.

She'd liked Uncle Charlie, though. He'd sat in his old rocking chair on the veranda and rocked backwards and forwards very slowly, watching the children playing in the garden, while his housekeeper, Mrs Manners, went backwards and forwards setting the big old table for tea.

"Please . . . would you like me to help?" Sheena asked once, coming across from where they'd been playing under the trees.

Mrs Manners shook her head. "You're here to enjoy yourselves, dear," she said, "I'll manage this."

Sheena had looked at her uncle timidly. "Can I get you anything, uncle?" she asked, but he'd just made a funny snuffling sound, as if he was asleep.

Caroline Maxwell had lurched up to the veranda then with two rackets and a handful of tennis balls.

"Hey, you!" she called loudly to Sheena. "Come on! You're wanted to make up the numbers for tennis!"

"I don't know how to play," Sheena said quietly, "and . . . and could you speak a bit more softly? Uncle's asleep."

"He's always asleep!" Caroline boomed. She ran round the side of the house. "That silly goose in there can't play tennis!" Sheena heard her shout to someone.

●

When the veranda and the garden were silent again and Sheena was putting the tea-plates round the table, just for something to do, her uncle opened one eye.

"I wasn't asleep, m'dear," he said. "Just dreaming."

Sheena smiled shyly.

"That's what this old chair's for — dreaming in. I get all sorts of special dreams while I'm sitting in it."

Sheena was just going to say something but Giles Chartwell-Smyth appeared from round the corner.

"They've sent me to ask if tea's ready," he said. "We're all absolutely starving."

"Won't be long . . . won't be long," Uncle Charlie said.

"I expect it's that Mrs Manners holding things up," Giles said. "Staff are awful these days. Mother had to sack one maid only last week. Perfectly useless, she was."

●

When Giles had gone off and it looked as though her uncle had gone to sleep, Sheena tiptoed away and went round to the side of the house to watch the tennis match — but it hadn't got very far because everyone was rowing.

"I'm not playing!" Arabella Maxwell said, storming away. "You lot cheat!"

"I don't! And I didn't want to play anyway!" Susanna Chartwell-Smyth said.

"I didn't want to *come* here," Caroline Maxwell said.

"Neither did *I*," Giles retorted, "but mother said we had to because uncle's very old and he might leave us something in his will."

"We've heard he's got some hidden treasure in the house," Emmeline Chartwell-Smyth said. "I'm going to look for it."

Sheena didn't want to hear any more. She went indoors again and Mrs Manners allowed her to load up the tea trolley with cups and saucers.

Teatime was a general excuse for showing off, seeing how much you could eat and saying 'Ugh, we don't have *this* at home!' and Sheena kept looking at her feet and feeling terribly embarrassed. Her cousins might be well-dressed and well-travelled but they had no manners at all!

Since that day back in the summer, Sheena and her mother had heard no more from Uncle Charlie (though Sheena had written to him to say thank you for having her, of course), until the letter came from Mrs Manners to say that Uncle Charlie had died.

●

A month after that, Sheena's mother got a letter from a firm of solicitors, asking if Sheena would 'kindly attend a reading of Uncle Charlie's will, where she might hear something to her advantage.'

"Well!" her mother said, "the family will be out in force for *that* — they'll be hoping to get their hands on Uncle Charlie's treasure."

"*Is* there a treasure?" Sheena asked curiously. "Emmeline seemed to think there was."

Her mother laughed. "There was supposed to be a lot of jewellery years ago," she said, "But I think it's all just a family rumour. You go along, though — maybe your uncle's left you a picture or a nice ornament or something."

So Sheena went. Her cousins were there, of course, looking Sheena up and down and whispering loudly about what she was wearing, and Sheena sat on her own and pretended not to notice.

A man from the solicitors was there with Mrs Manners. He lined all the cousins up on chairs in front of him and explained exactly what Uncle Charlie had wanted everyone to have. The house, apparently, was to go to Mrs Manners (there was a long drawn-out gasp of disgust from Giles at this), and Arabella and Caroline's father was to get Uncle Charlie's big car.

The children came next. Susanna got two oil paintings ('Worth a fortune!' Sheena heard her say) and Emmeline

got a Ming vase. Sheena wasn't quite sure what a Ming vase was but noticed Emmeline giving her sister a triumphant look, so she thought it might be something better than two oil paintings. Arabella got a huge antique table and chairs, Caroline got some real silver candlesticks and Giles got Uncle Charlie's coin collection.

It was Sheena's turn. She waited with baited breath, wondering where they would put silver candlesticks or a piece of Uncle's huge furniture in their little house.

'To Sheena, I leave my rocking chair,' the solicitor read out, and there was a moment's

silence and then all the cousins burst into noisy laughter.

"*That* old thing!" Giles said.

"Shows what he thought of *you*!" Arabella said rudely.

"Bet it's got woodworm!" Emmeline finished.

Sheena's eyes stung with tears — not because she was disappointed in what her uncle had left her, but because of the cruel comments from her cousins.

"It's a lovely old chair!" she said as loudly and convincingly as she could. "Uncle called it his dreaming chair and I'm glad he left it for me. I wouldn't know what to do with a vase!"

"No-one got the treasure!"

Giles said before his sister could hush him up. "Bet the mean old thing's hidden it away somewhere!"

Mrs Manners said that she'd make arrangements for Sheena's chair to be delivered to her the next day.

"Your uncle was very fond of that chair, you know," she said to Sheena when she was seeing her out. "He'd never let just anyone sit in it. He said it had magic powers!"

Sheena smiled politely, feeling sure that Mrs Manners was just saying that to make her feel better about only getting the old chair when everyone else had got valuable things. . .

●

When the chair arrived the following day Sheena's mother had forty fits.

"Really!" she said, "I would have thought your uncle would have thrown that out years ago. It's in terrible condition!"

Sheena stared at the old chair. It *did* look rather scruffy — all its varnish was scratched and worn, the wooden rockers were battered-looking and the canework at the sides of the seat was broken in.

"It's practically falling to pieces!" her mother went on. "You don't really want to keep it, do you?"

"Of course I do!" Sheena said. "Uncle Charlie left it for me specially. I can't just throw it away."

"Well, I don't want it down in the sitting room," her mother said. "You'll have to leave it upstairs."

Sheena hauled it up to her room and put it at the end of her bed. She had to admit it looked pretty funny in there, sitting among the white-painted modern furniture.

In the days that followed, her mum pushed it into various corners of Sheena's room 'so it won't look quite so obvious' she said, but whichever position it was in, it always seemed to be in the way.

"I really think it will have to go!" she said to Sheena one morning after laddering her tights on the scratchy wood. "It just gets in our way, and it's not even nice to look at!"

"But uncle left it to me!" Sheena said. "I can't sell it!"

"You can bet that your cousins have sold what *they* were left and pocketed the money," her mother said. "Not that anyone would want to buy that chair. You'd have to give it away!"

"I can't! Uncle would be so hurt."

"It's not as if it's even useful!" her mother said.

"It isn't supposed to be useful. Uncle used to call it his dreaming chair."

Her mother sniffed. "Your uncle always was a strange old chap!"

That night Sheena couldn't sleep. She lay awake looking at the chair in the ray of moonlight streaming through the gap in the curtains.

I suppose I'll have to get rid of you, she thought sadly, especially if you're just going to make Mum moan at me.

The chair seemed to creak softly, a little sound of protest.

'I don't want to,' Sheena said to it silently, 'but this room's really not the right sort of place for you to be.'

The chair seemed to look back at her reproachfully — and for a second Sheena almost thought she could see Uncle Charlie sitting there, rocking himself gently.

●

She tossed and turned, still unable to sleep, and then it suddenly occurred to her that Uncle Charlie had seemed to have no trouble falling asleep in the chair, so maybe it would do the same for her . . .

She got out of bed and pulling the duvet after her, climbed into the chair. It began to rock straight away, hardly needing any effort from Sheena to keep it going.

All at once she seemed to find herself back in her uncle's house — and yes, there was Uncle Charlie at the door waving to her and smiling. It was like a dream, yet somehow Sheena knew she wasn't dreaming.

Sheena went in and Uncle Charlie led her downstairs into what had once been the wine cellar. Beckoning for her to follow, uncle went to a slab in the stone wall and seemed to lever a corner of it so that it came out in his hand. Sheena peered into the little square hole that it left. It was almost pitch black in the cellar but — one of those strange things that can only be explained by it being a dream — Sheena found she could see quite easily.

Sheena gasped in amazement! Inside the hole was an oval bowl filled with jewellery — rings, bracelets and necklaces. Gold and silver, diamonds, sapphires and emeralds flashed and sparkled in front of her eyes. Without being told, Sheena knew that she had found the long-lost family treasure!

●

Her uncle turned to look at her face and laughed at the expression on it, then he turned back to the jewellery and pointed to a small brass plaque set into the wall above it. 'For the owner of the rocking chair' it said.

Sheena gave a cry of delight and surprise — it was such a loud cry that she woke up.

The rocking chair was still moving gently. The rocking chair . . . the dreaming chair. Now Sheena knew why her uncle had left it to her!

She could hear that her mother was still up so she jumped out of the chair and ran downstairs as fast as she could. Maybe it wasn't too late to go round to Uncle Charlie's house right then and claim the treasure that was hers . . .

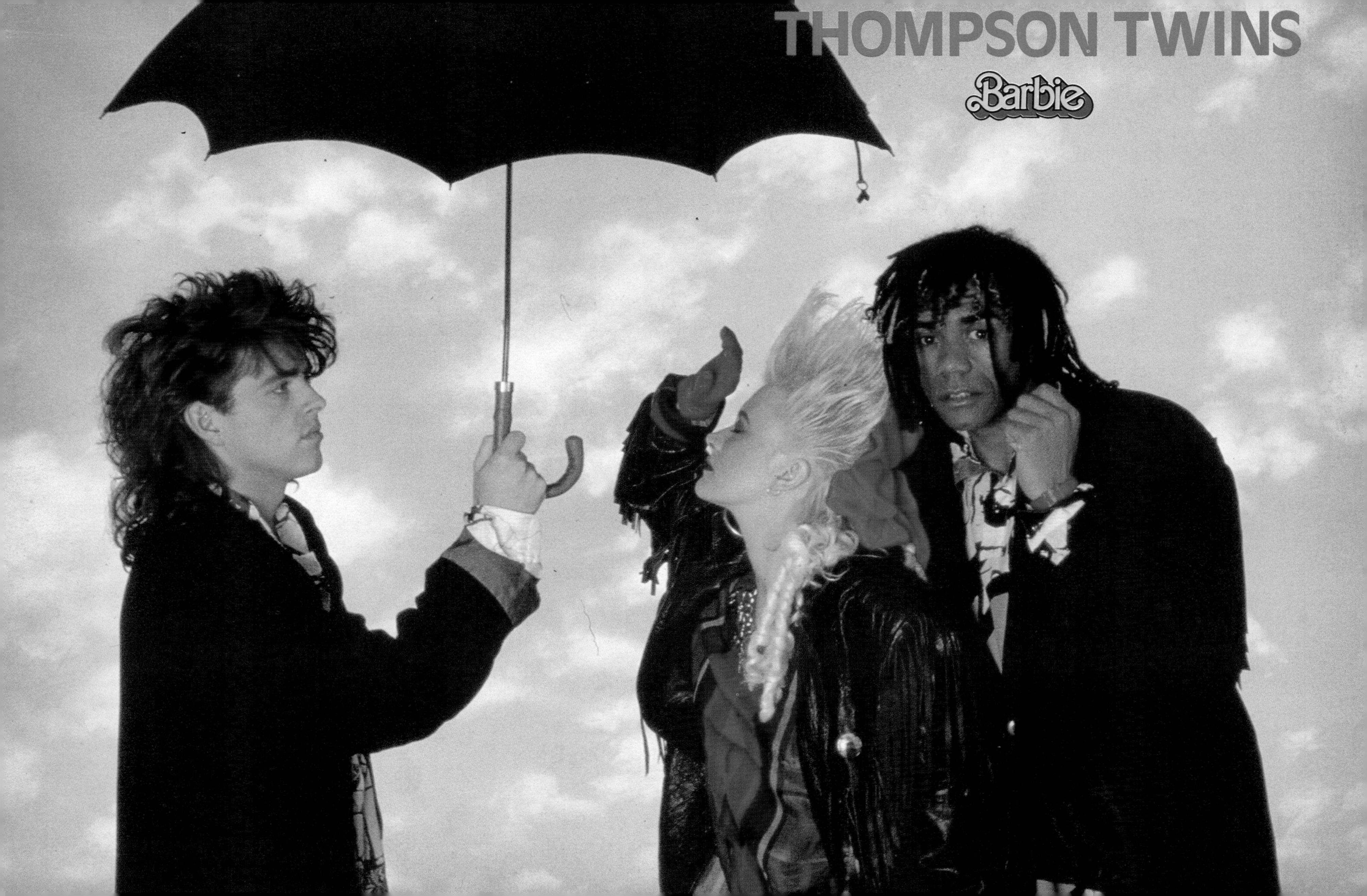
THOMPSON TWINS
Barbie

BARBIE'S BEAUTY QUIZ

Test your knowledge here and see if you're likely to end up with the beauty queen title.

Just answer true or false

1. Greasy hair should only be washed once a week. F

2. Washing your face with soap is bad for your skin. F

3. You should always squeeze spots and pimples. F

4. You don't need any more than eight hours sleep a night. F

5. Eating foods like sweets, crisps and cakes will keep your skin clear. F

6. As long as you use a sun tan lotion you can lie in the sun for as long as you want. F

7. A very hot, steamy bath will make you feel terrific. T

8. Cleaning your teeth morning, night and after meals will help to protect them. T

9. Eating lots of meat, cheese, cream and eggs is good for you. T

10. You should try and exercise every day. T

11. Jacket potatoes aren't fattening. T

12. It's a good idea to bathe or wash all over every day. T

ANSWERS

1. As long as you use a mild shampoo, you can wash greasy hair every day if necessary.

2. Make sure you use the right soap for your skin and you shouldn't have a problem.

3. Never squeeze spots and pimples — you'll cause a scar.

4. Most adults need at least eight hours sleep a night. Children need a lot more.

5. Avoid these foods like the plague for clear skin!

6. Even if you use a sun tan lotion with a high protection factor, you must never stay out in the sun for long. Start with half an hour, then build it up gradually.

7. A warm bath is much better for you than a hot one. You'll only end up bright red and uncomfortable.

8. If particles of food are left in between your teeth, this can lead to tooth decay. So brush them after every meal if you can.

9. Try and eat a balanced diet. Meat, cheese, cream and eggs all contain a lot of fat which isn't good if you eat a lot of it.

10. It's a very good idea to try and exercise every day — you'll feel better.

11. Jacket potatoes aren't fattening until you add lots of butter to them.

12. Get into the habit of having a daily bath or shower to keep fresh and clean.

Three or less correct answers: Well, there's not much chance of you ending up with the beauty queen title, is there? I think you'd better start reading the beauty pages in the Barbie Magazine and then you may gain a few tips.

Make sure you don't forget the correct answers, will you?

Four to seven correct answers: Hm, you're not too bad when it comes to the beauty stakes, but there's still some room for improvement.

Brush up on your knowledge about eating, hair and skin, and you'll look and feel like a million dollars.

Eight or nine correct answers: You're not doing badly, but you just haven't made it to the top yet, have you? It looks like you'll be taking the runner-up prize, but with a bit more effort, you'll soon know all that's necessary to get full marks, so have a go!

Ten to twelve correct answers: Well, you're obviously going to be the one taking the beauty title. Well done! You know the best way to plan a beauty routine and you've got all your facts right.

You must have been reading up all the beauty pages in all the magazines. Just remember to keep up the good work!

TEARS FOR FEARS

Curt Smith and Roland Orzabel make up the magical duo Tears for Fears who have produced hit after hit.

Both were born in Bath, Avon in 1961, which makes them 26 and they've been the best of pals since their childhood days.

Although they're rich and famous now, they both share unhappy childhood experiences of living on a council estate in Bath and always being short of money — but that's all behind them now.

Both Curt and Roland married at an early age and still live in Bath with their wives — but in very different houses to those early days.

CAT LOVERS

Curt has five cats called Treasure, Garp, Ben, Charlie and Emmy.

Roland is also a cat lover and owns one with a really daft name. Can you believe it's Zero Algebra Waldorf Churchill — what a mouthful!

Curt's favourite food is his wife's homemade onion soup but Roland prefers Indian or Japanese food along with Campari.

FAN CLUB:

c/o Outlaw, 2nd Floor, 145 Oxford Street, London, W.1

How does Barbie manage to look so good? Read on and follow her tips ...

Every evening, before Barbie goes to bed, she lays out the clothes she is going to wear the following morning. This saves her rushing around trying to find everything when she gets up.

Barbie never leaves her clothes lying in a heap on the floor. She always hangs everything up or puts her dirty clothes in the laundry basket.

Always check that you haven't got any buttons missing or that your hem isn't coming down before you put your clothes away.

One day a week, usually at the weekend, Barbie sets some time for cleaning all her shoes and boots. It's not one of her favourite jobs, but she knows how important it is to look after her footwear.

If Barbie goes on a modelling assignment or a special date with Ken, she always pops a spare pair of tights into her bag.

This way, she's prepared if she should ruin the pair she's wearing.

When you're out choosing clothes with Mum, make sure that the outfit you like really suits *you* and you're not just choosing it because your best friend has got something similar.

Never wear anything that's too tight, loose, short or long, just because it happens to be in fashion. Wear things that suit your body shape. Don't wear a style if

FASHION SECRETS

you don't feel happy wearing it. Barbie is very tall and thin, so she can wear lots of different styles. Very few people have model girl figures so they have to learn to choose clothes which suit their own figures.

If you've got clothes in your wardrobe which you know you are never going to wear again, ask Mum if you can swap them with your friends for something in their wardrobe. But do check with Mum first!

ARE YOU A TRUE FRIEND?

1. A friend lets you into a big secret. Do you:
(a) Keep it a secret and tell no-one?
(b) Broadcast it around the school?
(c) Tell just one person — well you know they won't tell anyone else!

2. Your best friend is always being told how pretty she is by all your other mates. Do you feel:
(a) A tiny bit jealous?
(b) Pleased — you're her biggest fan!
(c) Green with envy? You could scratch her eyes out. *5*

3. It's your birthday party and one of your friends is really miserable and it's spoiling everyone else's fun. Would you:
(a) Tell her to cheer up or go home?
(b) Go out of your way to get her more *10*

Are you nice to know? Are you a good friend to have? Try our quiz and we'll soon see . . .

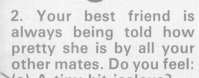

involved with the party games?
(c) Ignore her and make sure everyone else is joining in with the fun and games?

4. Some bullies at school are picking on your best friend. Do you:
(a) Stick up for her no matter what?
(b) Stay away — you don't want to get into any trouble?
(c) Tell a teacher so as they can sort it out? *10*

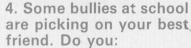

5. If you have got friends coming round after school, would you:
(a) Make them cakes

and buns?
(b) Tidy up your bedroom before mum gets in?
(c) Tell them to bring their homework so you can copy it?

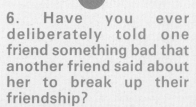

6. Have you ever deliberately told one friend something bad that another friend said about her to break up their friendship?
(a) Yes — but you shouldn't have done?
(b) Yes — you felt left out?
(c) No? *10*

SCORE

1. a (10) b (0) c (5)

2. a (5) b (10) c (0)

3. a (5) b (10) c (0)

4. a (10) b (0) c (5)

5. a (10) b (0) c (5)

6. a (0) b (5) c (10)

Barbie and the rock stars —
Derek and Diva.

NOW FIND OUT HOW YOU RATE
AS A TRUE FRIEND:

0-15: Have you any friends? If you do you won't have them for much longer! Try not to be so selfish and be a little nicer. You'll find it will work to your advantage — it's nice to have lots of friends around.

20-40: I don't think your friends have too much to worry about — you can certainly class yourself as a good friend to have. You know not to let your friends take advantage of you but you would always help them out.

45-60: You are certainly a true friend. Your friends are lucky to have you around — but make sure they don't take you for granted too much because it's obvious you're a bit of a softy and it certainly shows!

THE GIRL WHO TOLD STORIES

"We'll be going to America for our holidays," Emily said, lying on the grass next to me in the park.

I sat up and looked at her enviously. "You lucky thing!"

"We're going to Disneyland and the Space Centre and that place with all the splashy water slides and Niagara Falls and *everywhere*."

"How long are you going for, then?"

"Two weeks," she said promptly.

"You'll never see that lot in two weeks," I said, flopping down again. "I don't know much about geography but Niagara Falls and Disneyland are miles from each other."

I felt her looking at me. "Oh well," she said carelessly. "We might leave out a couple of places."

■

"Bet you're not really going at all!" I said, but she jumped up saying she wanted me to go to the kiosk with her to get an ice cream and pretended not to hear me.

I sat on the wall and watched her queuing up and kicked myself for believing her in the first place. Emily was always making up stories — mostly about her house and her relatives and the things she got bought for her, and at first I'd listened open-mouthed. There were stories about her being related to stars and how they'd come to her house for tea, stories about the places she'd visited and the things she'd done, stories about the fantastic house she lived in — with the suite of rooms specially for her.

Because she'd only just come to live in our town and I'd only met her in the holidays I didn't know anything about her background, so at first I'd believed every word she said. I really liked her, you see, in spite of her stories. She was funny and interesting and always had great ideas for playing games.

■

She never asked me home to see this fantastic house, though, we always played in the park or at my place. One day I got so curious about it that I followed her home when she left the park. I had some idea that she lived up Strawberry Hill, where the huge houses had gardens that led to the river, and I was dying to see which one it was.

To my surprise, though, she walked down a tiny lane alongside a factory and went into a little two-up and two-down house that backed straight onto the railway. It was a tiny little place, like a doll's house, and just the opposite of what I'd been imagining.

I didn't say anything to her, but after that I took everything she said with two pinches of salt. I still enjoyed the stories, and as long as I didn't believe them they were quite entertaining.

She came back from the kiosk holding a huge ice cream with a chocolate flake in it, and another one for me.

"You shouldn't have!" I said. "I've already had one today — and anyway I can't pay you back. I've spent all my pocket money for this week."

"Oh, that's all right," she said airily. "My rich uncle came over last night — he's in the pop business, did I tell you? — and he gave me loads of money to spend."

"Really?" I said.

She pulled out the flake and bit it. "He's terrifically rich. Always gives me money. He can get autographs, too, I've got loads."

"I'd like some autographs," I said. "Could he get me George Michael's, d'you think?"

"Oh, not George Michael's," she said quickly, "that's the wrong label."

"Well, how about . . . ?"

"Actually, he's going abroad soon," she interrupted. "I don't think he'll be able to get them any more."

"Oh," I said, and I smiled to myself. Another story!

■

"When we've finished the ices shall we go to your house and play records?" she asked then.

"We could go to yours, for a change."

"Oh no, my mother's entertaining," she said straight away. "A cocktail party or something. We wouldn't be welcome."

"Okay, then, we'll go to mine," I said.

It was the day after, when Emily started talking about the

little door in the wall. We were in the park as usual and sitting on a seat watching the ducks on the pond.

"I saw it when I was coming to the park this morning," she said excitedly. "I came along the high street and took the short cut by the church. Well, in the wall there was this dear little door . . . "

"In the wall?" I asked. "Don't you mean in the church?"

"No, that's just it," she said. "The door was in the wall — and I've often walked that way but I've never seen it before."

I shrugged. "Perhaps you've never really looked."

"Well, I've opened it and peeped in!" she said, and her eyes gleamed. "It was a beautiful, beautiful garden, full of fantastic flowers and plants and lovely trees all in blossom. In the distance there were fountains and a great big palace, glittering in the sun."

I started giggling, I couldn't help myself. "Honestly!" I said. "I like your stories but you can't expect me to believe *that*!"

"But really, *really* I saw it."

"Oh yes!" I said. "You'll be telling me next that you saw Cinderella going up towards the palace in a golden coach."

"No, no, of course I didn't!" she said crossly.

"Why didn't you go in there — through the door, then?"

Her face fell. "I wanted to," she said. "I nearly did go in — and then I remembered you were waiting for me. I had a funny feeling that if I went in I wouldn't get out again."

I stared at her. Her stories didn't usually end like that — though I still didn't believe her, of course.

"Well, how about going together now, then?" I asked. "I'd like to see this little door."

"That's just it! I shut it again and started running up the path towards here, and then I

59

changed my mind, thought I *would* go in after all. The thing was, when I turned back and tried to find it, it had disappeared."

I started giggling again. This was more like her. "Next time, go in and pick some of those exotic flowers and bring them to show me," I said. "And then I might believe you."

"I told you, if I go in I go for good," she said. "You might not see me ever again."

That Saturday I saw Emily in the high street in town. I was just coming out of the supermarket with Mum and she was over the road. I nearly went up to her but something stopped me. I think it was because I knew I'd have embarrassed her. She had a couple of younger children with her, one in a push chair, and was looking really tired and miserable. She carried a huge bag of shopping in one hand and had a plastic bag of washing in the other and was trying to manage these and the younger children without much success.

I thought to myself that she'd never ever mentioned having brothers or sisters and had let me think she was an only child. She'd also said that her mother had her own little sports car that they went shopping in and a woman to do the washing and cleaning!

I looked at her and decided that her home life couldn't be very happy . . . maybe that was why she was always making up stories.

A few days later I saw Emily in the park again as usual. We spent a while trying to haul some planks of wood up an oak tree to make a tree-house, then just sat around on the grass talking about school and which lessons we liked best.

"Have you seen your door again?" I asked when we'd run out of things to talk about.

She looked at me a bit oddly.

"I wasn't going to tell you . . . "

"Why not?"

"Because I knew you wouldn't believe me."

"Oh, go on," I said: "I like hearing your stories."

"It's *not* a story!"

"All right, then, it's true," I said. "Go on — tell me!"

"Well," she started, "I have seen it again, but not in the same place."

"What? Had it moved?"

She nodded. "I saw it when I was walking back from my aunt's house on Monday. It was in a wooden fence — one of those they put up temporarily when workmen are doing up a site."

"Was it the same door, though?" I asked curiously. This was a really good story.

"Just the same. A little door in shiny wood with a curved top and big brass handle."

"And did you look in?"

"Yes!" She was quiet for a little while — thinking up even more fantastic stories, I thought.

"Go on, then!" I urged her.

"Well, it was more or less the same as before. The flowers and trees and everything, with the palace far away, but this time I could see animals playing."

"What — wild animals?"

She shook her head. "*Nice* animals. Cats and kittens frisking about. I really wanted to go in there and play with them."

"Haven't you got a pet?" I asked, prepared for her to say she had a pony of her own and any number of cats and dogs.

"No," she said. "I'm not allowed any."

"Not *allowed*! I thought you could have anything you liked at home. In that great big house," I added wickedly.

"No . . . no, Mummy's allergic to fur," she said quickly. "I say to her — all the fur coats you've got and I can't

even have a pet rabbit! She says mink's different, though."

It would be! I thought. "So what about the door?" I asked, returning to the story. "Why didn't you go in?"

"I nearly did," she said, "but I had a lot of shopping and . . . "

"I thought you were coming back from your aunt's?"

"I was. I did the shopping on the way. I had all the stuff for tea, you see, and I knew Mummy would go mad if I didn't get it back in time, so I just shut the door and went on."

"And did it disappear?"

"Yes." She sighed. "I looked back when I got to the end of the road and it had completely vanished. No sign of it at all."

"You should have gone in," I said. "And brought me back a kitten!"

"You don't understand," she said. "You don't even believe me."

"Well, honestly, you don't really expect me to . . . "

"I didn't want to tell you. You asked," she said pointedly.

She didn't mention the door for a few days after that — she was too busy talking about the house, the wonderful house her uncle was buying, with its own stables, she said, and the horses she was going to be allowed to ride as much as she liked — but eventually I asked her if she'd seen the door again.

"Only for a minute," she said. "I had to go to the doctors to collect something for Mummy and I saw it on the other side of the road. I was late and I didn't even have time to glance in it."

I remember we were sitting on the swings while we were talking and she suddenly jumped straight off and pointed over to the other side of the pond.

"It's over there now!" she said. "I can see it!"

"What's there? Not the door?!"

"Yes! It's in the wall of the old pavilion halfway along under the window. I can see it!"

I screwed up my eyes, and looked where she was pointing. *Was* there the faint shape of a door, or was I imagining it?

"Come on!" she said. "I'll prove to you it's there. Let's go and open it!"

I laughed and looked at my watch. "I haven't got time," I said, "I've got to be in for tea at five o'clock and it's almost that now."

"Just come and *look* at it," she urged.

"It'll take ages to walk round there," I said. "I can't be bothered." Especially for something that wasn't even *there,* I felt like adding.

"Well, I'm going," she said. "And I'm going right in there this time." She started walking away.

"See you tomorrow?" I called.

"Maybe. Maybe I won't be back," she replied over her shoulder.

I walked home and when I got in found that my cousin had come round to show me his new puppy, so I thought no

more about Emily and the little door that evening.

The next day — and for a week after that — I was in bed with chicken pox and feeling too groggy to think about anything at all. It was ten days before Mum let me out again.

■

I went straight round to the park to look for Emily, but although I waited around for the rest of the day, didn't see her. She wasn't there the next day, either, so I walked round to where she lived — only to find the house shut up, its curtains pulled tightly together. I knocked and knocked but no one came and I saw that there were some newspapers pushed through the letter box lying on the mat inside, as if they'd been gone some days.

I went back to the park and began to walk round the pond, wondering what had happened. There was something at the back of my mind that was worrying me. Suppose Emily had been telling the truth for once? Suppose there had been a door and she'd gone through it . . .

But no, of course there couldn't have been! I walked right round the pond to the old cricket pavilion where she'd said it had been. There was nothing there, of course, no trace of a door in its green-painted side.

■

I stopped dead. There, right at my feet, was a hanky, a pale-blue hanky. I bent and picked it up, it had a dark-blue 'E' embroidered in the corner — and was lying exactly under the window of the pavilion.

It's been over three months now and I've never seen Emily again or found out what happened to her. I don't think I'm ever going to know whether her story about the door in the wall with the land of flowers and castles and kittens is true. Somehow, for Emily's sake, I'd like it to be!

62

SPANDAU BALLET

Spandau Ballet made their first live performance in London during November 1979. They released their album 'True' back in 1982. It was so successful it sold millions of copies in 22 different countries.

Since then Spandau have produced hit after hit and have gained a huge following of loyal and devoted fans.

All five members of the band — Gary, Tony, John, Steve and Martin went to Owens Grammar School in Islington, North London.

Gary and Martin Kemp, who are brothers, also attended the Anna Scher Theatre School in their younger days — which came in handy for them because since then they've both done a bit of acting.

Martin was the last member to join the band. Apparently at school the teachers thought he was a very promising footballer, so he started to train with Arsenal — but he soon gave it up when he decided he wanted to be a pop star — we reckon he certainly made the right decision.

However, brother Gary knew from an early age that he wanted to be in the music business. He received his first guitar at the age of eleven — a birthday present from his parents, and as well as playing the guitar, Gary also writes all the material for Spandau Ballet.

Lead-singer Tony Hadley worked as a warehouse man and a printers assistant before joining the band. Quite dull really in comparison with his life today. But Tony is probably the quietest member of the band. He enjoys a quiet social life with wife Leonie and young son Thomas, but he does enjoy horse riding and playing football. He also loves Indian food.

John Keeble the drummer left school to work in a bank, but he didn't stick it too long before he joined up with the rest of the band.

His favourite hobbies are socialising and messing about with cars, but he has a secret fear of spiders!

We don't think spiders would bother Steve Norman too much — he loves animals. Steve has a dog and a piranha fish which he calls Frank in the Tank.

Birthdays

Gary James Kemp — Guitar and backing vocals — October 16th 1959. Libra.
Tony Patrick Hadley — Lead vocals — June 2nd 1960. Gemini.
John Keeble — Drums — July 6th 1959. Cancer.
Steve Norman — Sax and percussion — March 25th 1960. Aries.
Martin Kemp — Bass — October 10th 1961. Libra.

Fan Club Address

Spandau Ballet
c/o Jacqui Quaiffe,
Suite 7,
89 Great Portland Street,
London, W.1.

Barbie is so busy rushing around from one job to another that she has very little time left for sports and hobbies. But when she does find the occasional half an hour to relax, does she put her feet up and take it easy? No, not a chance. You'll either find Barbie out on the tennis courts, riding her horse, Prancer, or swimming in the pool.

When the weather makes sure that Barbie has to stay inside, she either goes through her exercise routine in the gym, goes for a rehearsal with the Rock Stars, or plays with Fluff and Prince.

If Barbie has had an exhausting week, she likes to go for a long drive in the country.

This helps her to relax and forget about her next modelling assignment until she gets back to town. Sometimes she will take Skipper or Ken with her, but she often likes to go by herself.

And when Barbie is in a fun mood she'll go for a quick trip on her Splash-Cycle along the beach.

BARBIE ON THE MOVE!

DEBBIE'S DEAREST FRIEND

Spooky Special

OH, NO...
HE'S THERE
AGAIN!

DEBBIE, WHAT'S
WRONG? WHY DID YOU
SCREAM OUT?

I — I SAW HIM AGAIN,
IN THE MIRROR.
THAT AWFUL CLOWN —
THAT REFLECTION!

HE'S BEEN THERE FOR MONTHS NOW. EVERY TIME I
SEE MY OWN REFLECTION HE'S THERE, BEHIND ME,
SMILING!

YOU DO
BELIEVE ME,
DON'T YOU?

OF COURSE
WE DO, DEAR.

THEY DON'T BELIEVE ME, AND
NEITHER DOES ANYONE AT SCHOOL...
BUT HOW CAN I BLAME THEM? IT MUST
SOUND AS IF I'M CRAZY..!

BUT I'M SURE YOU'RE JUST
HAVING NASTY DREAMS — NOW
BACK INTO BED WITH YOU, LOVE.

But at school next day...

OH, NO..!

And even on
the bus...

HE'S HAUNTING
ME ALL THE
TIME NOW!

That night...

THERE'S NOTHING NASTY ABOUT HIM, EXCEPT
THAT HE REALLY DOESN'T EXIST... BUT WHY
DO I KEEP SEEING HIM? IT'S AS IF HE WERE
TRYING TO TELL ME SOMETHING...

WHAT'S
WRONG,
DEBBIE?

At breakfast . . .

COULD IT POSSIBLY HAVE SOMETHING TO DO WITH MY REAL PARENTS, DO YOU THINK?

HOW COULD IT, DEAR? WHEN WE ADOPTED YOU, YOU HAD NO MEMORY OF YOUR PARENTS. FOR YOU THE PAST JUST DID NOT EXIST.

IT STILL DOESN'T EXIST, BUT I DON'T MIND. YOU'RE AS LOVING TO ME AS ANY REAL MUM COULD HAVE BEEN.

But sometimes she had felt a little sad, wondering about her unknown past . . .

AND NOW THERE'S THE CLOWN HAUNTING ME. IT'S GETTING SO THAT I'M SCARED TO LOOK IN A MIRROR . . .

IT'S SUCH A LOVELY DAY . . . PERHAPS IT HAS JUST BEEN MY SILLY IMAGINATION ALL THE TIME . . !

But as she reached the shops . . .

OH, NO! HE'S THERE AGAIN — REFLECTED IN THAT WINDOW!

I MUST GET AWAY . . . HIDE FROM MY OWN REFLECTION — AND HIS!

IF I SEE NO REFLECTIONS, HE CAN'T KEEP FOLLOWING ME . . . I'LL STAY HERE WHERE I'M SAFE . . !

THE END

TOP OF THE POPS!

Test your pop knowledge and astound your friends — hopefully by showing them how good you are! Ready, Steady, Go!

1. What instrument is Howard Jones famous for playing?
(a) Drums
(b) Guitar
(c) Synthesiser

2. Martin and Gary Kemp of Spandau Ballet both appeared in Jackanory.
True or False?

3. What is George Michael's nickname?
(a) Trog
(b) Yog
(c) Bog

4. Stephen Tintin Duffy started out playing with Spandau Ballet.
True or False?

5. What is Prince's favourite colour?
(a) Red
(b) Pink
(c) Purple

6. The Eurythmics once had a hit about a year. What year was it?
Clue — George Orwell

7. What is the name of the lead of U2?
(a) Beano
(b) Bruno
(c) Bono

8. Match these artists with the bands they play:
1. Tom Bailey
2. Tony Hadley
3. Paul Weller

(a) The Style Council
(b) The Thompson Twins
(c) Spandau Ballet

9. Which part of the U.S. does Madonna originally come from?
(a) Washington
(b) Detroit
(c) Miami

10. What video did Michael Jackson appear in as a werewolf?
(a) Billie Jean
(b) Beat It
(c) Thriller

11. Paul King of King used to be a policeman before becoming famous.
True or False?

12. Fill in the missing words to these Wham hits:
(a) Club . . .
(b) I'm Your . . .
(c) . . . Me Up . . . You . . .

CHECK YOUR ANSWERS HERE

1. C — Synthesiser
2. True
3. B — Yog
4. False. He played with Duran Duran
5. C — Purple
6. 1984
7. C — Bono
8. 1 — B, 2 — C, 3 — A
9. B — Detroit
10. C — Thriller
11. True
12. (a) Club Tropicano
(b) I'm Your Man
(c) Wake Me Up Before You Go Go

HOW DID YOU GET ON?

Under 4: *I'm afraid I don't think Radio 1 will be signing you up just yet! Snap up. You must do better.*

5 – 8: *You're no fool, you've got your pop facts at your finger tips. Keep up the good work.*

9 – 12: *Top marks! Mike Read's got nothing on you — you're definitely 'Top of the Pops'.*

GIRL OF THE FOREST

The cruel wire of a snare closes around a slender leg, and a cry echoes through the forest — the frightened cry of a wild creature in pain!

And its mother is desperate — unable to help her young one and sensing that danger approaches . . .

Violence is something unknown to her. Always the forest has been a place of quiet beauty and peace — but now . . .

In this moment of blind terror, the deep-rooted instinct for survival proves too strong.

HUH . . . MISSED THE CRITTER!

YEAH, BUT WE AIN'T DONE SO BAD. I KNOW A ZOO THAT'LL PAY REAL HANDSOME FOR THIS LITTLE BEAUTY.

LEAVE HIM, PETE — I'LL LAY YER ODDS HIS CRIES'LL BRING HIS MOTHER BACK HERE AGAIN.

COULD BE YOU'RE RIGHT, KANE — WE'LL WAIT AN' SEE.

But in the shadows of the forest . . .

DO NOT GRIEVE, STAR. I SAW WHAT THEY DID, BUT YOU SHALL HAVE YOUR BABY BACK AGAIN — AND THEY WILL PAY FOR THEIR CRUELTY!

A few minutes later . . .

SOMETHING MOVING IN THOSE TREES — TOLD YER SHE'D COME BACK!

I WON'T MISS THIS TIME!

But . . .

THERE, BEHIND THAT TREE!

GOOD GRIEF . . . !

I — I'LL SWEAR IT WAS A GIRL. DID YOU HIT HER?

DUNNO — BUT COME ON!

IT IS A GIRL!

WHAT'S A KID DOING OUT HERE IN THE BACKWOODS ALL ALONE?

HOW WOULD I KNOW, BUT SHE CAN RUN LIKE A DEER HERSELF — LET'S GET HER!

TOO RIGHT, WE WILL!

THINK OF THE MONEY WE'D MAKE FOR BRINGING IN A REAL WILD GIRL!

TELEVISION ALONE WOULD PAY A BOMB FOR HER . . . !

SHE'S TOO FAST FOR US. SHE'LL GET AWAY!

OH NO, SHE WON'T . . . !

OH . . . OH NO!

NO . . . KEEP BACK . . . !

As dawn comes again, two frightened men make their escape . . .

I THOUGHT THEY WERE GOING TO KILL US, BUT SHE MADE THEM LET US GO — WHO WAS THAT GIRL?

NO-ONE'S BEEN UP THERE IN THE WOODS FOR YEARS, SINCE . . .

THAT'S RIGHT. I REMEMBER NOW. A YOUNG HUSBAND AN' WIFE WERE KILLED — BUT WHAT ABOUT IT?

SINCE A LIGHT PLANE CRASHED UP THERE EIGHT ODD YEARS BACK.

THEIR KID, A GIRL OF FIVE, WAS MISSING. THEY SEARCHED FOR DAYS, BUT HER BODY WAS NEVER FOUND.

YOU — YOU DON'T THINK . . . ?

WE'LL NEVER KNOW — AND EVEN IF WE DID, WHO WOULD EVER BELIEVE US?

IT'S ALL RIGHT, MY BROTHERS AND SISTERS. THEY'LL NOT BE COMING BACK.

WE CAN LIVE IN PEACE AGAIN NOW!

THE END

73

Barbie had been asked to appear in an advertisement — and Ken was one of the photographers. . .

WHAT SORT OF PLACE ARE WE GOING TO BE FILMING IN, KEN?

WELL, KINGSVILLE MANOR IS OWNED BY LORD CHARVIL, BUT HE'S OUT OF THE COUNTRY AT THE MOMENT. IT'S A SUPER OLD HOUSE WITH LOTS OF RICH FURNISHINGS. . .

PERFECT FOR THE HOUSE-HOLD PRODUCTS WE'VE GOT TO ADVERTISE!

THE HAUNTING AT KINGSVILLE MANOR

THE ONLY THING IS. . .I HOPE WE'RE OUT OF THERE BY NIGHTFALL. WHEN I VISITED IT TO MAKE ALL THE ARRANGEMENTS IT FELT KIND—OF SPOOKY AFTER DARK. . .

OH, GO ON WITH YOU!

YOU AND YOUR IMAGINATION, JENNY!

YES, I SUPPOSE IT'S JUST ME BEING SILLY AGAIN.

IT SOUNDS AN INTERESTING PLACE. I THINK I'M GOING TO ENJOY TODAY.

Kingsville Manor was very beautiful. . .

WOW!

IT'S QUITE A PLACE, ISN'T IT?

IMAGINE LIVING HERE!

And just like a palace inside. . .

WELCOME TO KINGSVILLE MANOR!

YOU MUST BE MRS CANNINGS, THE HOUSEKEEPER.

74

LORD CHARVIL TOLD ME TO MAKE YOU WELCOME AND SAID YOU WERE TO BE ALLOWED TO FILM ANYWHERE YOU LIKED.

THAT'S VERY KIND, MRS CANNINGS — BUT I THINK THIS HALL WILL BE PERFECT FOR MOST OF OUR SHOTS.

IT'S JUST LIKE BEING TAKEN BACK IN TIME... ALL THESE BEAUTIFUL THINGS.

AND THIS FANTASTIC SUIT OF ARMOUR. IT MUST HAVE BEEN MADE FOR A GIANT!

OKAY, BARBIE, STOP DAYDREAMING! IT'S TIME TO GET INTO YOUR OUTFIT.

COMING, BILL!

And a short while later...

I THOUGHT I WAS GOING TO BE LADY OF THE MANOR — NOT THE MAID!

READY, BARBIE?

OKAY, BARBIE, CUE!

IF YOU'RE LOOKING AFTER A RATHER SPECIAL HOUSE, YOU'LL NEED RATHER SPECIAL CLEANING MATERIALS...

YOU'LL FIND PRECIOUS PRODUCTS MAKE EVERYTHING YOU NEED!

FROM ANGORA DUSTERS TO REAL BEESWAX POLISH — PRECIOUS PRODUCTS MAKE SOMETHING TO SUIT!

GOOD...GOOD...NOW LET'S TAKE IT FROM THE BEGINNING AGAIN.

And after a few hours filming...

OKAY, EVERYONE — GREAT! TAKE A BREAK NOW AND WE'LL DO SOME MORE AFTER LUNCH.

THANK GOODNESS FOR THAT! I'M FED UP WITH DUSTING AND I'M DYING TO LOOK AROUND...

After a quick sandwich lunch Barbie wandered off...

I'M SURE MRS CANNING WON'T MIND — SHE SAID WE COULD GO WHERE WE LIKED...

AND I'M DYING TO SEE THE BEDROOM — OOH! I KNEW THEY'D HAVE FOUR-POSTER BEDS!

And afterwards Barbie went to look at the kitchen...

I'M JUST LOOKING ROUND, I HOPE YOU DON'T MIND.

THAT'S QUITE ALL RIGHT, MISS. I'M EMMA, ONE OF THE MAIDS.

HAVE YOU WORKED HERE LONG?

YEARS AND YEARS, MISS. SOMETIMES IT SEEMS LIKE I'VE BEEN HERE FOREVER.

I SUPPOSE THERE'S ALWAYS A LOT TO DO...SO MANY THINGS TO BE KEPT CLEAN AND SHINY — THAT SUIT OF ARMOUR ON THE STAIRS, FOR INSTANCE.

FUNNY YOU SHOULD MENTION THAT, MISS.

WHY'S THAT, EMMA?

WELL, THERE WAS NEARLY A TERRIBLE ACCIDENT BECAUSE OF THAT ARMOUR...

A YOUNG MAN VISITOR IT WAS... HE WAS STANDING WITH HIS BACK TO THE STAIRS WHEN THE ARMOUR SUDDENLY BEGAN TO TOPPLE OVER. IT WOULD HAVE FALLEN ON HIM BUT SOMEONE JUST MANAGED TO PUSH HIM OUT OF THE WAY AT THE LAST MOMENT.

IT WOULD HAVE KILLED HIM, NO DOUBT ABOUT IT. I GOT ONTO MASTER TO HAVE THE ARMOUR MOVED OFF THE STAIRS AFTERWARDS, BUT HE SAID HE LIKED IT THERE — THAT IT HAD STOOD THERE FOR OVER A HUNDRED YEARS.

MAYBE IT'S SAFER NOW. YOUR MASTER PROBABLY MADE IT MORE SECURE.

THEY COULD NEVER MAKE THAT SUIT OF ARMOUR SAFE. IT KILLED IN THE PAST — AND IT WILL GO ON KILLING!

OH CRUMBS...I WISH I HADN'T BROUGHT THE SUBJECT UP.

WELL. . .ER. . .I'D BETTER BE GOING, I'VE GOT THE REST OF THE HOUSE TO SEE.

IT WAS NICE TO TALK TO YOU, MISS.

But Barbie found it difficult to concentrate on the rest of the house. . .

I CAN'T GET WHAT EMMA TOLD ME OUT OF MY MIND. . . SHE WAS SUCH A STRANGE, OLD-FASHIONED GIRL, TOO.

. . .and she was quite pleased when it was time to start filming again.

OKAY, BARBIE, WE'LL HAVE YOU STANDING HERE WITH A COUPLE OF TINS OF POLISH, I THINK.

RIGHT, BILL!

YOUNG EMMA OUGHT TO BE DOING THIS!

All went quite well until late afternoon. . .

THAT JUST WRAPS IT UP, I THINK. PERHAPS YOU COULD GET A FEW MORE STILLS BEFORE THE LIGHT GOES, KEN.

SURE THING!

Ken was checking something on his camera when. . .

THAT SUIT OF ARMOUR. . . I THINK IT'S MOVING!

KEN! MOVE!

WHAT THE. . .

IT ALMOST SEEMS TO BE TAKING A STEP FORWARD. . .

HEY! HEY – LOOK OUT!